CLACTON – FEB 2016

D1646335

Please return this book on or before the date shown above. To renew go to www.essex.gov.uk/libraries, ring 0345 603 7628 or go to any Essex library.

Essex County Council

Essex County Council

3013021143093 8

Original Korean text by Eun-seon Han
Illustrations by Mi-sook Yun
Korean edition © Yeowon Media Co., Ltd.

This English edition published by big & SMALL in 2015
by arrangement with Yeowon Media Co., Ltd.
English text edited by Joy Cowley
English edition © big & SMALL 2015

All rights reserved

ISBN: 978-1-925234-14-5

Printed in Korea

The
Farmer's Dream

Written by Eun-seon Han Illustrated by Mi-sook Yun
Edited by Joy Cowley

big & SMALL

An empty land...

0   Zero

Farmer Han had a dream of growing roses.

Farmer Han built five greenhouses.
The roofs of the greenhouses were shining.
He and his wife were so happy!

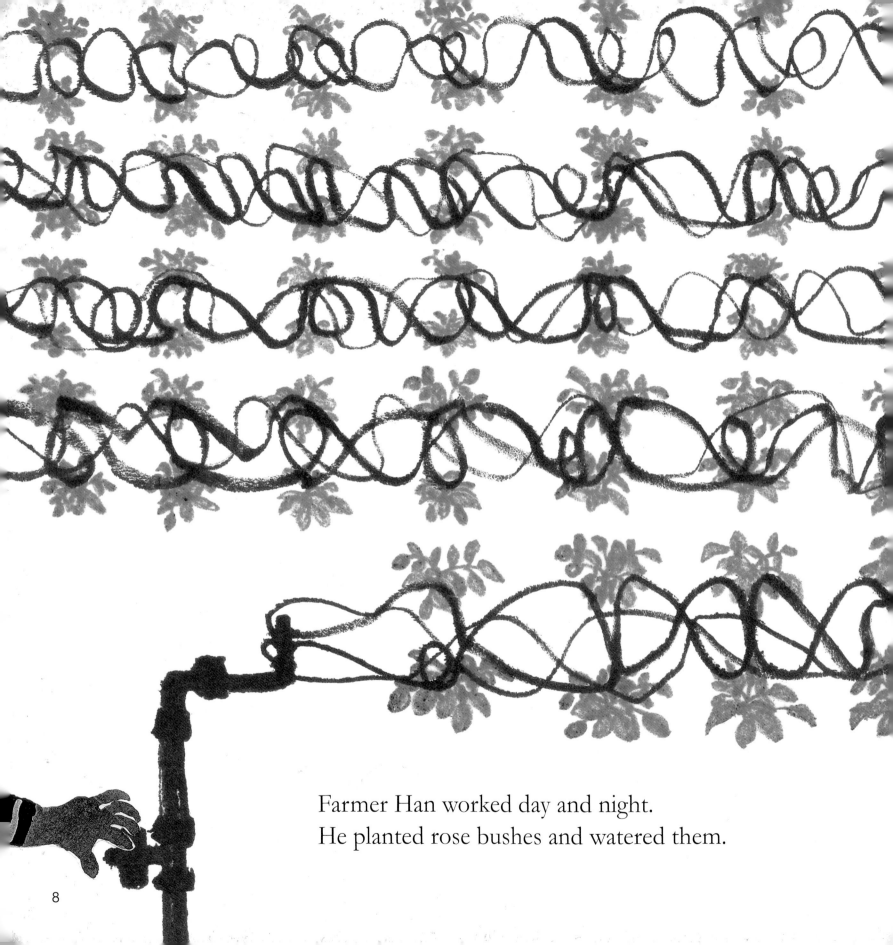

Farmer Han worked day and night.
He planted rose bushes and watered them.

8

On burning summer days,
he covered the glass roofs.
The rose bushes grew and grew.

The rose bushes grew as tall as Farmer Han.
They were as dear to him as if they were
his children. Now he had the first bud.

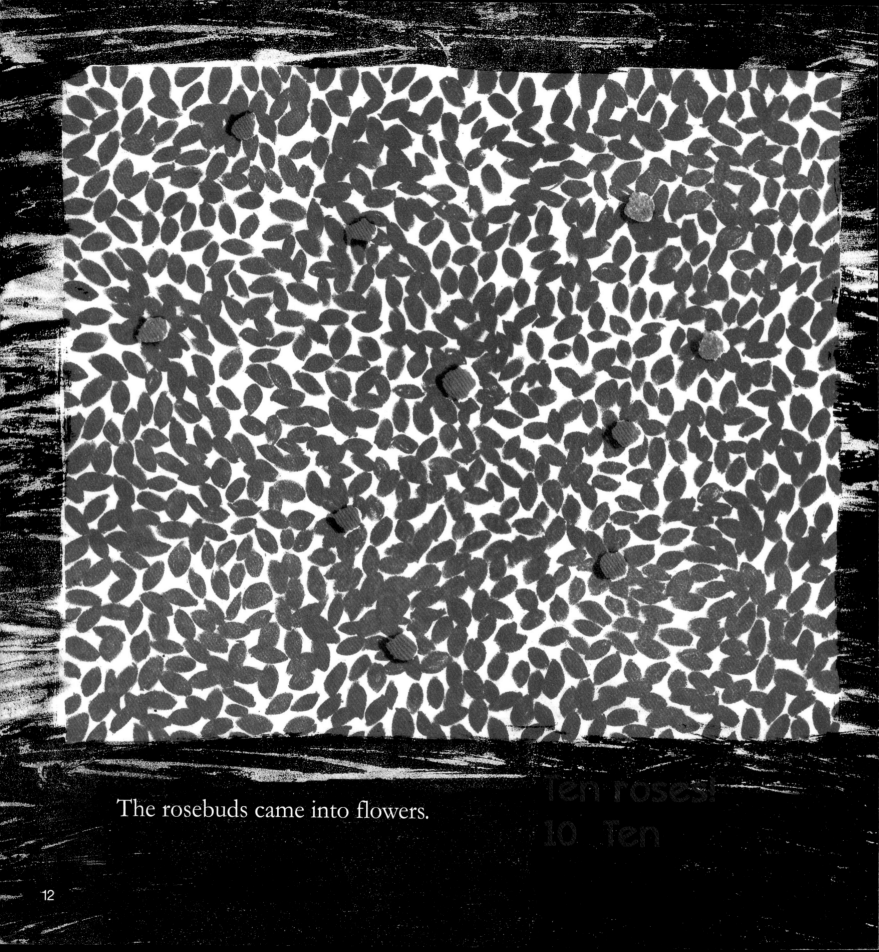

The rosebuds came into flowers.

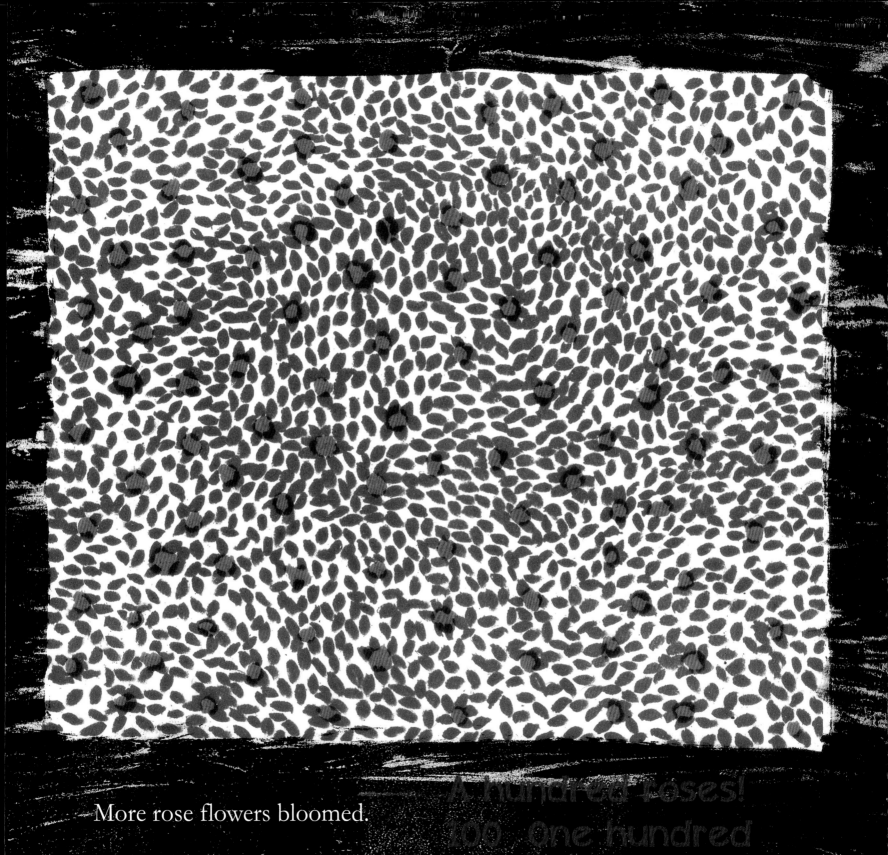

More rose flowers bloomed.

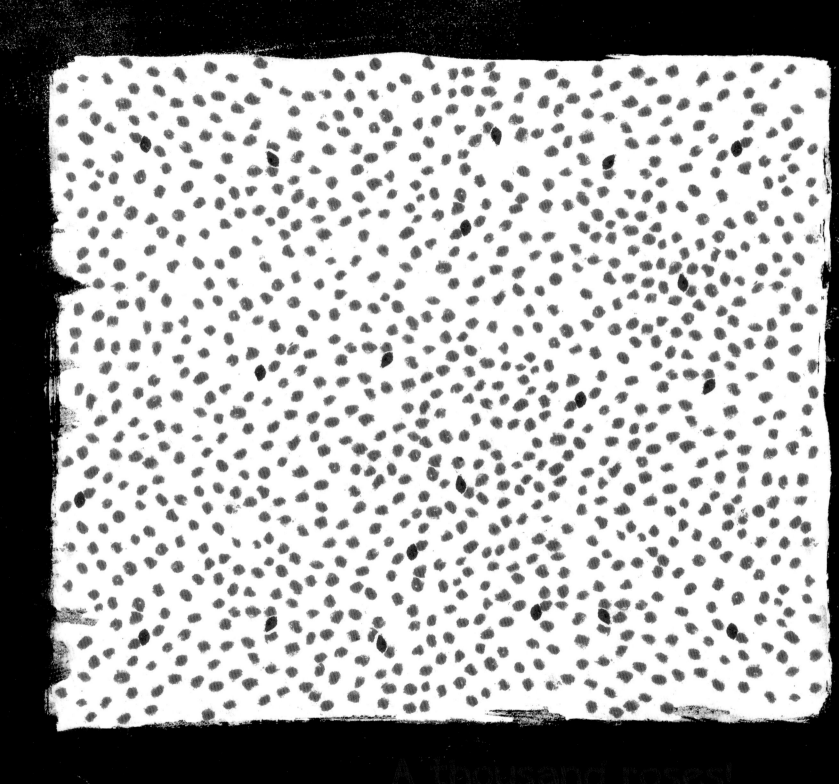

More and more rose flowers...

A thousand roses!
1,000 One thousand

More and more and
more rose flowers...

Ten thousand roses!
10,000   Ten thousand

The scent of roses filled the greenhouses.
Farmer Han picked the first roses and gave them
to his wife who had become a farmer with him.
He also gave roses to his friends.

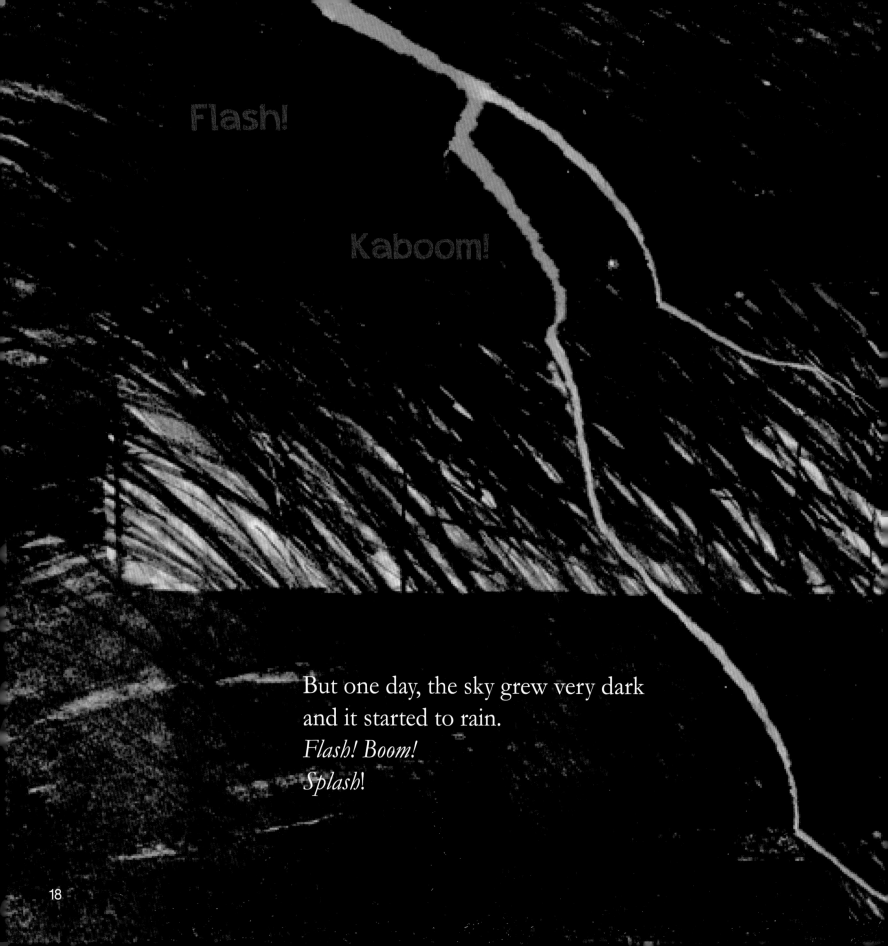

But one day, the sky grew very dark
and it started to rain.
Flash! Boom!
Splash!

Rain was poring down for three days.
The water in the river rose high
and swept into the greenhouses.

Splash!

The flood had swept away all the roses. Nothing was left. Even Farmer Han's beloved dog was missing.

Woof! Woof!

Farmer Han heard a sound came from inside of an oil tank. He and his wife looked in the oil tank. It was the missing dog, survived in oil and rain. Farmer Han no longer felt like giving up.

Farmer Han and his wife worked hard to clean out the greenhouses. They planted more rose bushes. *Dig, dig, dig! Scrape, scrape, scrape!*

The rose bushes grow again.
Grow, grow, grow!

One rosebud, again!
1 One

Farmer Han's heart beat fast
when he saw this new beginning.

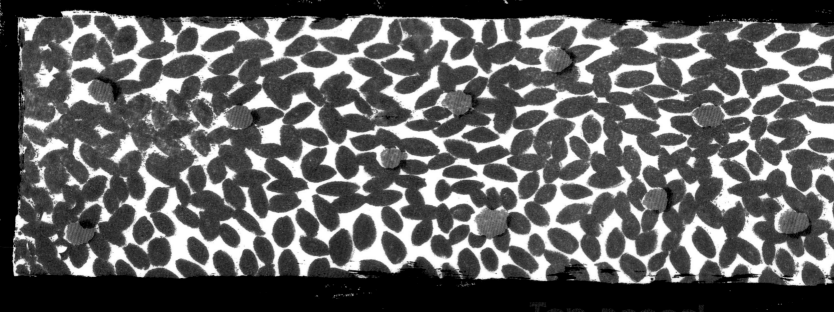

The rosebuds came
into flowers.

Ten roses!
10 — Ten

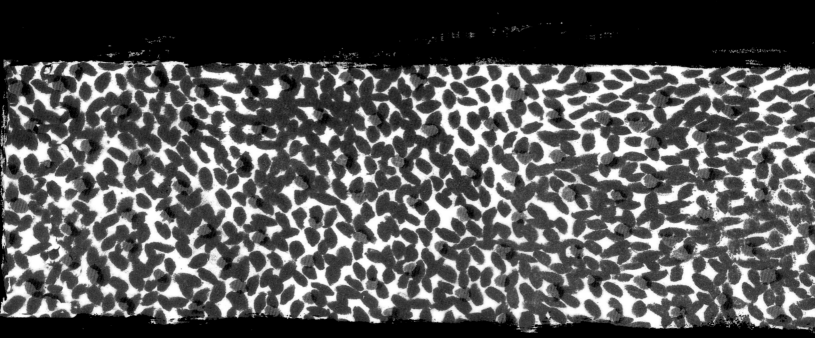

There were more roses bloomed,
more and more...

A hundred roses!
100 — One hundred

A thousand roses!
1,000   one thousand

Ten thousand roses!
10,000   Ten thousand

Farmer Han made his dream come true.
He was the happiest farmer in the world.

A Farmer Whose Dream Comes True

Following each picture, think about the meaning of zero and big numbers.

1

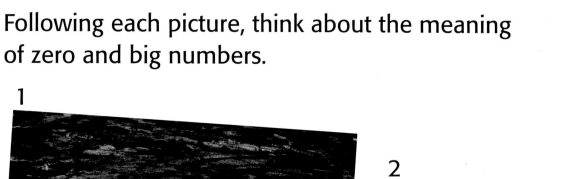

The empty land
(0   Zero)

Ten sparkling glass roofs
(10   Ten)

3

Pop! One rosebud
(1   One)

4

The scent of ten thousand roses fills the greenhouses.
(10,000   Ten thousand)

5

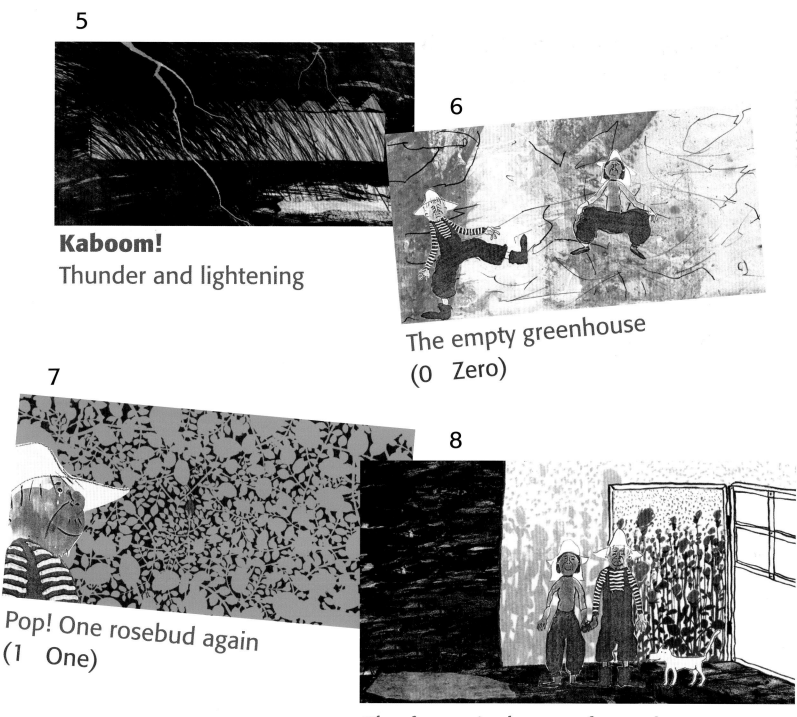

Kaboom!
Thunder and lightening

6

The empty greenhouse
(0 Zero)

7

Pop! One rosebud again
(1 One)

8

The farmer's dream of growing roses
comes true.

People Who Work Hard

In an empty field where there is nothing, some people are working hard, producing amazing things through toil and sweat.

The empty land. (0   Zero)

The man built strong, beautiful houses. (10   Ten)

The empty land. (0   Zero)

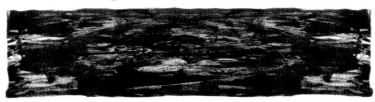 

The lady grew big red tomatoes. (100   One hundred)